Father Koala's
Nursery Rhymes

Kel Richards

illustrated by Glen Singleton

SCHOLASTIC
SYDNEY AUCKLAND NEW YORK TORONTO LONDON

For Shane and Sarah
who, years ago, inspired these verses
during many delightful reading-aloud hours—KR

For Janelle, for Dad—
for all your tall stories—
and for Ann B.   GS

Richards, Kel, 1946–.
    Father Koala's nursery rhymes.

    ISBN 0 86896 968 0.
    ISBN 1 86388 010 0 (pbk.).

    1. Nursery rhymes, English. I. Singleton, Glen. II. Title.

398.8

Text copyright © Kel Richards, 1992.
Illustrations copyright © Glen Singleton, 1992.

First published in 1992 by Scholastic Australia Pty Limited ACN 000 614 577,
PO Box 579, Gosford 2250. Also in Sydney, Brisbane, Melbourne, Adelaide
and Perth.

This paperback edition first published in 1992.

Reprinted in 1993 (twice), 1995 and 1996.

Typeset by Proset Imaging, Forresters Beach NSW.

Printed in Hong Kong.

12 11 10 9 8 7 6 5   6 7 8 9 / 9

Contents

Father Koala 4

Hot baked damper 6

Tom, Tom the piper's son 7

Gulargambone 7

Beyond the Black Stump 8

Wobbly wallabies 9

Into the land of the Never-Never 9

Jack and Jill went up the hill 10

Little Bo-Peep 10

Hickory, dickory dock 11

The bogong song 12

Blowfly, Blowfly 12

Hey diddle diddle 13

Swaggie put the billy on 13

Running through the mulga 14

Wombat, wombat 15

Clancy, Clancy 16

Clancy had a little brumby 16

The drover's wife 17

Matilda Possum 18

Creeping on tiptoes 19

Black swan song 19

It's raining, it's pouring 20

The station cook at Dunedoo 21

Sing a song of ten cents 21

Here we go 'round the banksia bush 22

Summer comes 22

Three fat chooks 23

Hello! Come in! G'Day! 24

Governor Bligh 24

Johnny Batman met a fat man 25

Crocodile, Crocodile 25

One, two, there's work to do 26

Baa baa, black sheep 27

Little Miss Golden 27

The Birdsville Track 28

Gone a-droving down the Cooper 29

Anzacs and lamingtons 30

Which is the way to Ballarat? 31

To Bondi 31

Old swaggie sun 32

Father Koala

Father Koala sits in the parlour,
Sipping a cup of tea.
We run to his side and he smiles with pride
And lifts us onto his knee.

'Oh take some time to make us a rhyme,
Oh Father Koala please!'
That's what we say in a playful way,
As we bounce upon his knees.

He clears his throat with a humming note,
Some six or seven times.
Then he drinks his tea, and he looks at me,
And he sings his gumleaf rhymes.

Hot baked damper!

Hot baked damper!
Hot baked damper!
With golden syrup covered thick,
Hot baked damper!

From the ashes of the camp fire,
For every little camper,
With golden syrup covered thick,
Hot baked damper!

The dripping syrup you can lick,
Your tummy you can pamper,
With golden syrup covered thick,
Hot baked damper!

When you're full then here's the trick,
Store some in your hamper.
With golden syrup covered thick,
Hot baked damper!

Tom, Tom the piper's son

Tom, Tom the piper's son,
Stole a pig and away he run.
Tom got caught, the pig got away,
And Tom went sailing to Botany Bay.

Gulargambone

Gulargambone, Gulargambone,
Please call me on the telephone.
Coolangatta, Coolangatta,
Tell me please what is the matter?
Goondiwindi, Goondiwindi,
Did you step upon a bindi?
Coober Pedy, Coober Pedy,
Taking all the cake was greedy!
Tallangalook, Tallangalook,
Tell me, are you feeling crook?
Daly Waters, Daly Waters,
Where's the present that you brought us?
Meekatharra, Meekatharra,
Plant the wheat of William Farrer.
West Wyalong, West Wyalong,
Come swimming in the billabong.
Narrandera, Narrandera,
Please come with me to Canberra.
Augathella, Augathella,
Climb the hill of Brindabella.
Kununurra, Kununurra,
Listen to the kookaburra!
Port Augusta, Port Augusta,
Now you've got me all afluster!

Beyond the Black Stump

Out beyond the Black Stump,
There are so many flies,
That if they take off all at once,
They black out all the skies.

Out beyond the Black Stump,
There are fleas as big as trucks,
And on the back of every flea,
Are several dingo pups.

Out beyond the Black Stump,
The mozzies roam in herds,
And their wings whip up a cyclone,
That's just too big for words.

Out beyond the Black Stump,
The dust goes whistling by,
And the crows out there fly backwards,
To keep the dust out of their eyes.

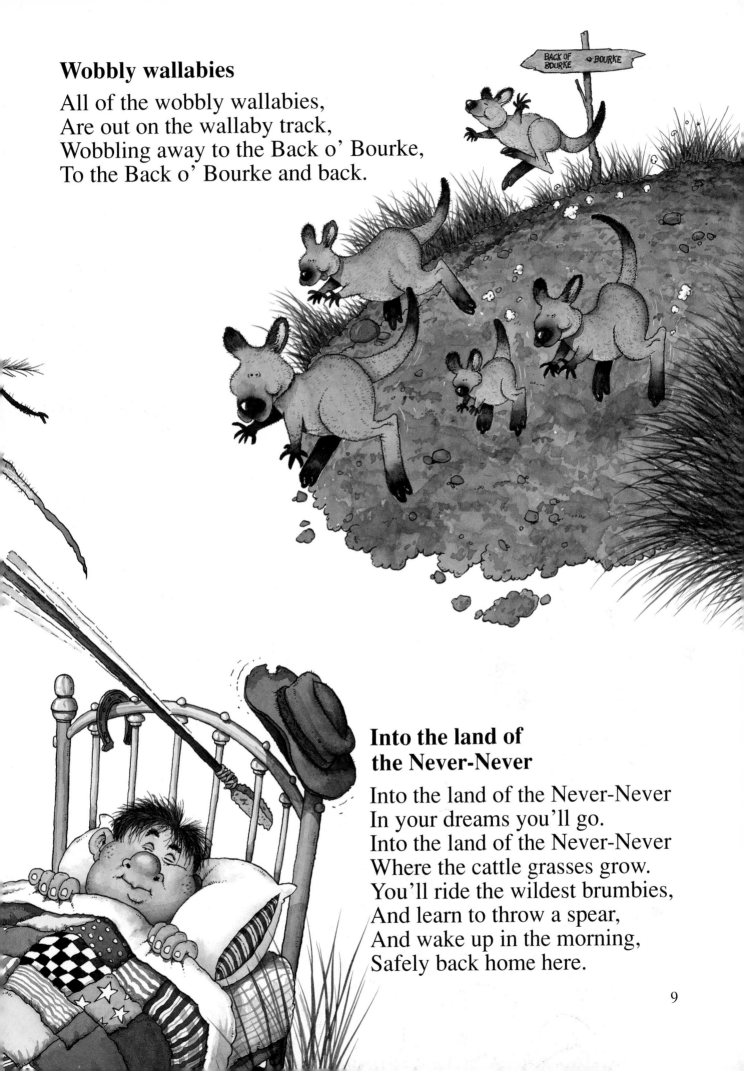

Wobbly wallabies

All of the wobbly wallabies,
Are out on the wallaby track,
Wobbling away to the Back o' Bourke,
To the Back o' Bourke and back.

Into the land of the Never-Never

Into the land of the Never-Never
In your dreams you'll go.
Into the land of the Never-Never
Where the cattle grasses grow.
You'll ride the wildest brumbies,
And learn to throw a spear,
And wake up in the morning,
Safely back home here.

Jack and Jill
went up the hill

Jack and Jill went up the hill,
To check the boundary fences.
Jack fell down upon the ground,
And nearly lost his senses.

The Jackaroo and Jillaroo,
Rode straight back home (of course!).
Jill carried Jack upon the back
Of her big, black gelding horse.

Little Bo-Peep

Little Bo-Peep has lost her sheep,
And watching them was her job.
But the kelpie pup will round them up,
And he will look after the mob.

Hickory, dickory dock

Hickory, dickory dock,
The drovers forgot their flock.
And all of the sheep
Fell fast asleep.
The kelpie dogs
Just slept like logs,
With noisy snores
And heads on paws.
Until the cry of a passing crow
Woke everybody down below,
Just like a loud alarming clock;
And the drovers rounded up the stock,
Hickory, dickory dock.

The bogong song

The bogong moth was passing through,
And as he passed he said, 'Hey you!
I'd like to linger longer,
In the city of Wodonga,
But the lady moth for whom I long,
Is far away on Mount Bogong.'
And with these words he flapped his wings,
And sang the song the bogong sings,
Then flew to one who'd waited long,
Upon the peak of Mount Bogong.

Blowfly, Blowfly

Blowfly, Blowfly,
Buzz away home.
Your babies are hungry,
Your babies all moan.
Blowfly, Blowfly,
Buzz away home.
Go back to your babies,
And *leave us alone*.

Hey diddle diddle

Hey diddle diddle, the banjo and the fiddle
Played for the dancing brolgas.
Who dance and sing through Alice Springs,
And up and down the Olgas.

Swaggie put the billy on

Swaggie put the billy on,
Swaggie put the billy on,
Swaggie put the billy on,
We'll all have tea.

Bunyip take it off again,
Bunyip take it off again,
Bunyip take it off again,
They've all gone away.

13

Running through the mulga

Running through the mulga,
Running through the scrub,
Running through the mallee,
Like a witchetty grub.

Running through the wattle,
Running through the trees,
Running through the blue gums,
Buzzing like the bees.

Hiding in the waratah,
Hiding up a tree,
Hiding in the bush,
So you can't see me.

Wombat, wombat

Wombat, wombat, fat and slow,
Digging with her fingers, digging with her toes,
Digging in the creek bank, digging in the hill,
Digging when it's windy, digging when it's still,
Digging in the sunshine, digging in the night,
Dig, dig, digging in the pale moonlight.

Clancy, Clancy

Clancy, Clancy dressed up fancy,
How does your paddock grow?
With kangaroos and tall emus,
And gum trees all in a row.

Clancy had a little brumby

Clancy had a little brumby,
A hardy mountain pony.
He'd ride him on the hillsides where
The ground was steep and stony.

The drover's wife

There was an outback drover's wife,
Lived in a wattle hut,
With seven children, a cattle dog,
A kitten and a pup.
There was a snake that tried to munch
Her children—so she killed it!
She baked it and she grilled it,
Then with sandwiches she filled it,
And she served it up for lunch.

Matilda Possum

Matilda Possum is sitting
Under the starry sky,
Up in the top of the ironbark tree,
Way, way, way up high.

Matilda Possum is listening
To the distant mopoke's cry,
Carried upon the whistling wind,
Way, way, way up high.

Creeping on tiptoes

Creeping on tiptoes, SSHHH! Don't be heard!
Spying on the dancing of Mr Lyrebird,
Dancing for the lady lyrebird to see,
The very secret dancing of his old corroboree.

Black swan song

Black swan swimming in the old billabong,
Black swan singing the black swan song.
Singing of the ocean, singing of the sea,
Singing her song to the coolibah tree.

It's raining, it's pouring

It's raining, it's pouring,
The farmer is snoring.
Wake the sheep! And wake the drover!
Now the heat and drought are over.

It's raining, it's pouring,
Has been all morning.
Drive the sheep to higher ground,
So they'll all be safe and sound.

It's raining, it's pouring,
The thunder is roaring.
Creeks are flooding! Rain is thudding!
Pass along the warning.

The station cook at Dunedoo

The station cook at Dunedoo
Cooked a pot of mutton stew
All on a summer's day.
A swaggie that was passing through
Stole that pot of mutton stew
And carried it far away.

Sing a song of ten cents

Sing a song of ten cents,
I never tell a lie,
Four and twenty kookaburras
Baked in a pie.
When the pie was opened
The birds began to laugh—
The gravy, meat and pastry:
They'd eaten nearly half.
The boss was at the homestead
Missing out on meals,
Out on the veranda
Squatting on his heels.
The cook was in the kitchen
Eating meaty pies,
Sitting on the windowsill
And beating off the flies.

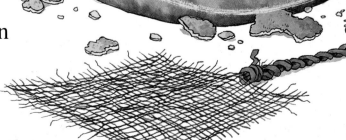

21

Here we go 'round the banksia bush

Here we go 'round the banksia bush,
Banksia bush, banksia bush.
Here we go 'round the banksia bush,
All on a summer's morning.

Looking around for gumnut babies,
Gumnut babies, gumnut babies.
Looking around for gumnut babies,
All on a summer's morning.

Running away from banksia men,
Banksia men, banksia men.
Running away from banksia men,
All on a summer's morning.

Summer comes

Summer comes,
Cicada hums,
Insect didgeridoo.
Dry heat, dusty heat,
One note, one beat,
All summer through.

22

Three fat chooks

Three fat chooks, three fat chooks,
Hear how they squawk, hear how they squawk.
They run all around with a waddling walk,
As we eat up their eggs with a knife and a fork,
And pieces of bacon and pieces of pork.
Three fat chooks!

Hello! Come in! G'Day!

Hello! Come in! G'day!
The ship sailed up the bay.
With Captain Cook and Mr Banks
And sailors lined up in their ranks.
They hit the ground,
And turned around,
And then they sailed away.

Governor Bligh

Governor Bligh swallowed a fly,
With his Vegemite on toast.
Said John Macarthur,
'That's who we're after!
The man that we dislike the most!'

Johnny Batman met a fat man

Johnny Batman met a fat man,
When he went exploring.
Said Johnny Batman to the fat man,
'Point me to Mount Warning'.

Said the fat man to Johnny Batman,
'This spot here is pretty.'
Said Johnny Batman to the fat man,
'I'll make this place a city!'

Crocodile, Crocodile

Crocodile, Crocodile,
Where did you go?
I went down to Sydney's
Big Royal Easter Show.

Crocodile, Crocodile,
What made you merry?
The bridge and the harbour,
And catching the ferry.

One, two,
there's work to do

One, two, there's work to do,
Three, four, there's more and more,
Five, six, with shovels and picks,
Seven, eight, work with your mate,
Nine, ten, we knock off then,
Eleven, twelve, work by yourself,
Thirteen, fourteen, wool needs sorting,
Fifteen, sixteen, gate needs fixing,
Seventeen, eighteen, dinner's waiting,
Nineteen, twenty, we've done plenty!

Baa baa, black sheep

Baa baa, black sheep,
Have you any wool?
Yes mate! Too right!
Three bales full.
 One for the shearer,
And one for the boss,
And one for your pullover
To stop you getting cross.

Little Miss Golden

Little Miss Golden worked on her Holden,
Changing the oil and grease.
When a yellow goanna,
Ran off with her spanner,
Miss Golden called up the police.

The Birdsville Track

The Birdsville Track is washed away,
Washed away, washed away.
The Birdsville Track is washed away,
My old drover.

The sun will dry it out again,
Out again, out again.
The sun will dry it out again,
My old drover.

Now it's dry and full of dust,
Full of dust, full of dust.
Now it's dry and full of dust,
My old drover.

Gone a-droving down the Cooper

Gone a-droving down the Cooper,
Are Clancy, Blue and Snow.
And they ride beside their cattle,
Where the western drovers go.

Gone a-shearing down the Lachlan,
Are Clancy, Blue and Snow.
And they shear their daily quota,
In a rhythm—blow by blow.

Anzacs and lamingtons

'Anzacs and lamingtons'
Say the bells of old Paddington.
'Hot pumpkin scones'
Say the bells of Toowong.
'Someone has nicked them!'
Say the bells out at Picton.
'I want them back'
Say the bells of Toorak.
'By next Wednesday arvo'
Says the big bell at Bargo.
'What's all the hurry?'
Say the bells on the Murray.
'They've all been eaten!'
Say the bells out at Leeton.
'Oh what a bungle!'
Say the bells of Rum Jungle.

Which is the way to Ballarat?

Which is the way to Ballarat?
With gold in the hills and gold in the flats.
Left, right, just like that,
That is the way to Ballarat.

Which is the way to Bendigo?
Where diggers dig for gold below.
Left, right, quick and slow,
That is the way to Bendigo.

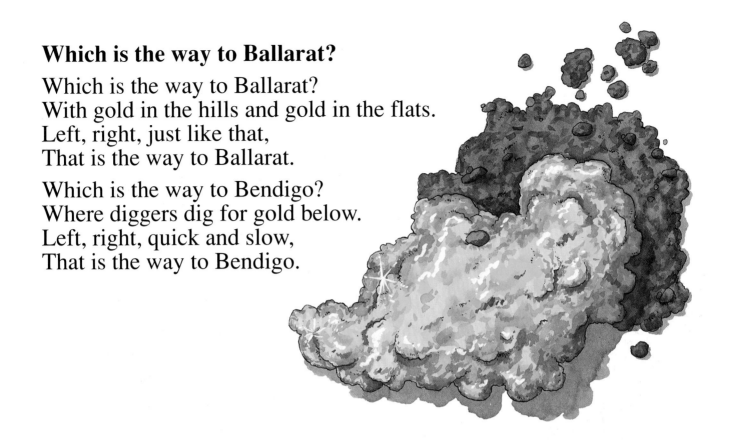

To Bondi

To Bondi, to Bondi,
To swim in the sea.
To Bondi, to Bondi,
My Grandma and me.

Home again, home again,
Shells in my hand.
Home again, home again,
Shoes full of sand.

Old swaggie sun

Old swaggie sun is tired,
His swag is far from light,
And over the western ridges,
He's camping for the night.

When you wake up in the morn,
He's in another place,
Tramping down the eastern road,
With a smile upon his face.